What Do You See?

Circle the things that are silly.

Kindergarten Scholar

This 😊 is **happy**. This 😞 is **sad**.

Happy is the opposite of **sad**.

Draw a line from each picture to its **opposite**.

slow

dry

wet

quiet

loud

fast

Opposites

Circle the picture that shows the **opposite** of the first picture in each row.

big

full

hot

in

Greater Than

Greater means **more than**.

4 is **greater than** 3.

4

3

Write how many there are in each group.
In each row, circle the set that is **greater**.

_____

- - - - - - - - - - - -

_____

- - - - - - - - - - - -

_____

- - - - - - - - - - - -

_____

- - - - - - - - - - - -

_____

- - - - - - - - - - - -

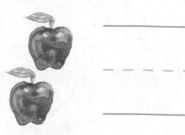

_____

- - - - - - - - - - - -

Make a set of  to show 1 **more than** 3.

How many ? _____

4

Less Than

Less means **not as many**.

2 is **less than** 3.

2   **3**

Write how many there are in each group.
In each row, circle the set that is **greater**.

 _____    _____

 _____    _____

 _____   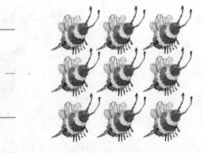 _____

Make a set of 🌙 to show 1 **less than** 10.

How many 🌙? _____

Kindergarten Scholar

This  is **big**. This  is **bigger**.

In each row, circle the picture that is **bigger** than the first picture.

Smaller

This 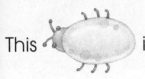 is **small**. This is **smaller**.

In each row, circle the picture that is **smaller** than the first picture.

Same Size

These  are the **same size**.

In each group, circle the two pictures that are the **same size**.

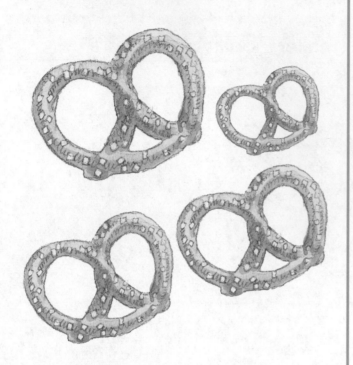 

Make a Pair

 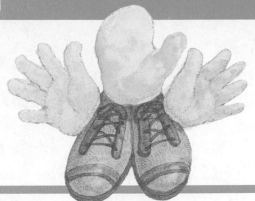

A and a and a make a **pair**.

A and a do not make a **pair**.

In each row, circle the two pictures that make a **pair**.

   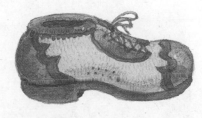

The tomato is on **top**.
The ants are on the **bottom**.

Circle the that is on **top**.

Circle the that is on the **bottom**.

 This is on the **left**.

 These are on the **right**.

left right

In each row, circle the picture that shows the **same direction** as the first picture.

left

right

Goat **rhymes** with **boat** .

In each group, circle the two pictures that **rhyme**.

In each group, circle the two pictures that **rhyme**.

What Goes Together?

 and **go together.**

In each row, circle the pictures that **go together.**

 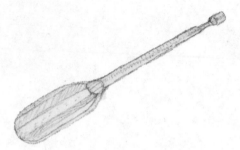 

What Goes Together?

In each row, circle the picture that **goes together** with the first picture.

Kindergarten Scholar

Sailing Through the Maze

Help the ship get to the dock.

BUNYAN WAS HER

START

DEPARTURE POINT

PIRATE'S LAIR

MOLE SHOAL

GREAT BIG ICEBERG

BACK COUNTRY

PINE FOREST

CORRAL REEF

PINE FRESHENER FOREST

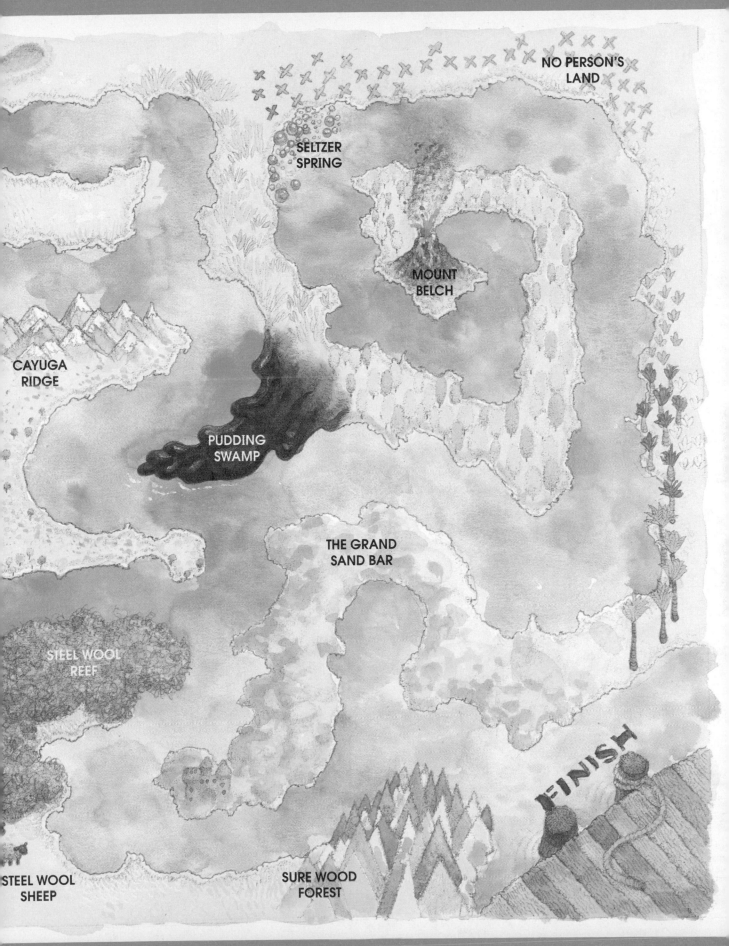

NO PERSON'S
LAND

SELTZER
SPRING

MOUNT
BELCH

CAYUGA
RIDGE

PUDDING
SWAMP

THE GRAND
SAND BAR

STEEL WOOL
REEF

FINISH

STEEL WOOL
SHEEP

SURE WOOD
FOREST

This 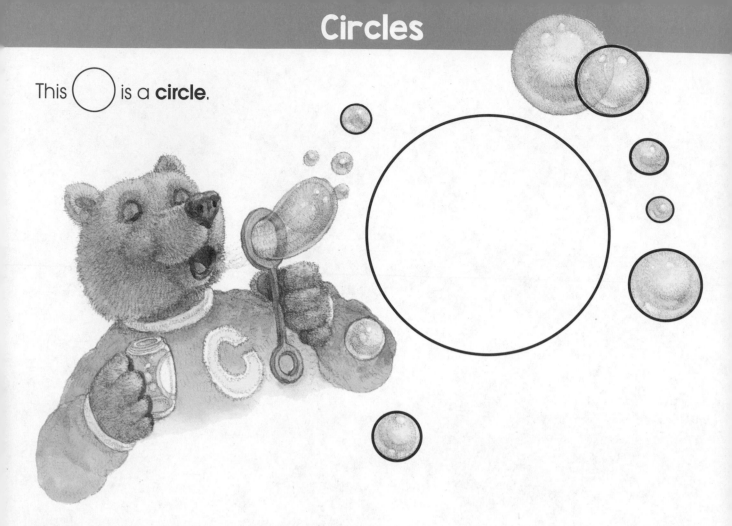 is a **circle**.

Color two circles **blue**.

Circles

How many ◯ can you find? _____

This ⬜ is a **square**.

Ahh! A square meal!

Color two squares **red**.

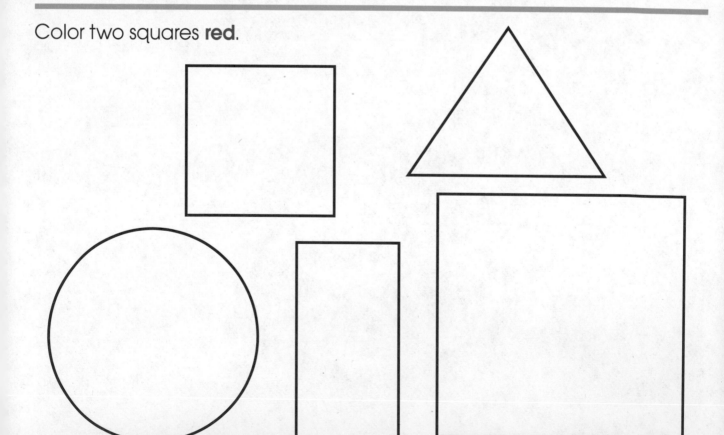

Squares

How many ☐ can you find? _____

This [ ] is a **rectangle**.

Color two rectangles **orange**.

Rectangles

How many ☐ can you find? _____

This 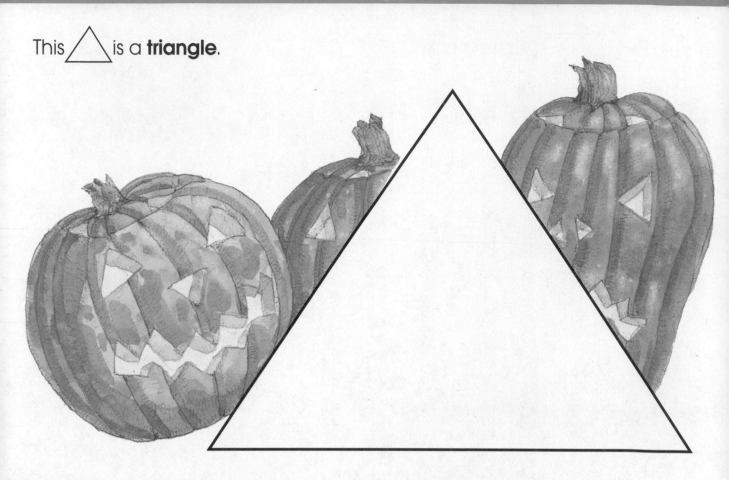 is a **triangle**.

Color two triangles **green**.

Triangles

How many △ can you find? _____

These  are the **same**.

In each group, circle the two pictures that are the **same**.

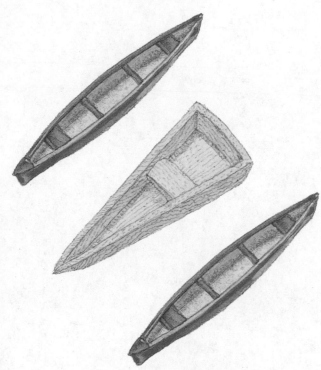

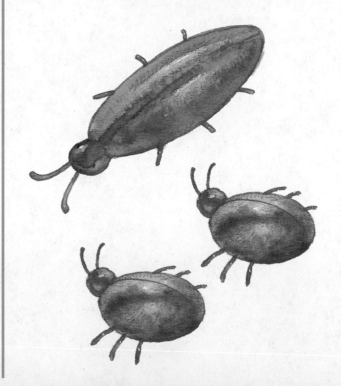

Same

In each row, circle the picture that is the **same size** as the first picture.

These  are the **same**. This is **different**.

In each group, circle the picture that is **different**.

In each row, circle the picture that is **different**.

First, Next, Last

Write **1** in the square to show what happened **first**.
Write **2** to show what happened **next**.
Write **3** to show what happened **last**.

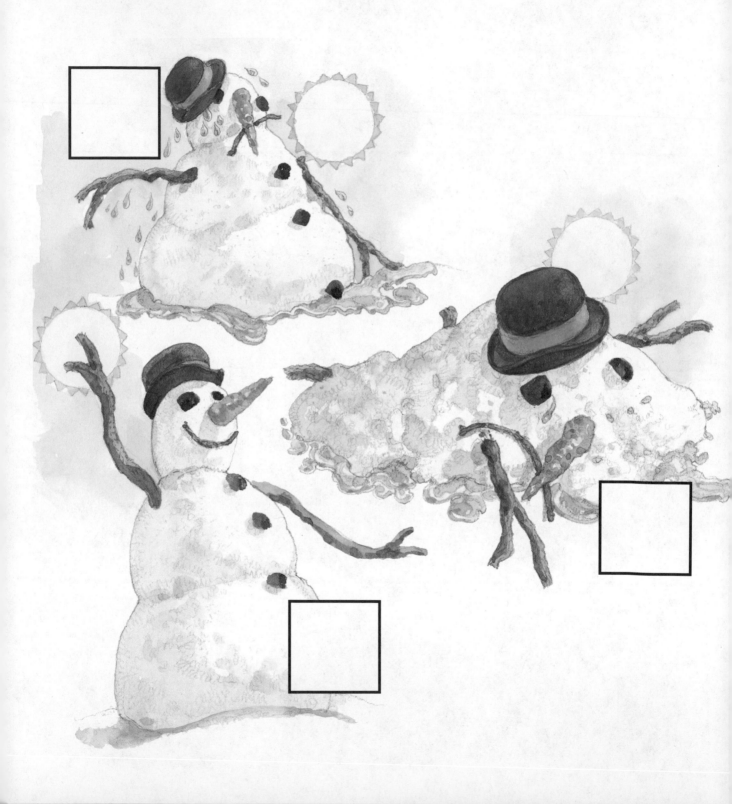

Write **1** in the square to show what happened **first**.
Write **2** to show what happened **next**.
Write **3** to show what happened **last**.

Write **1** to show what happened **first**.
Write **2** to show what happened **next**.
Write **3** to show what happened **last**.